Price Guide to American Cut Glass

Also by Dorothy Daniel

Cut & Engraved Glass—1771–1905:
The Collectors' Guide to American Wares

PRICE GUIDE TO AMERICAN CUT GLASS

by Dorothy Daniel

Drawings by Isador N. Steinberg

M. Barrows & Company, Inc.
Distributed by William Morrow & Co., Inc.
New York 1967

for Scoop

Published simultaneously in Canada by George J. McLeod Limited, Toronto.

Printed in the United States of America.

Library of Congress Catalog Card Number 67-25318

Contents

Introduction

For the more than 2000 years that glass has been decorated by abrasion, or cut by a turning wheel, it has been the shape of an individual or dominant motif that has been used to identify cut-glass designs.

Early-American glass was merchandised by its manufacturers as "one dozen nappies, Strawberry-Diamond" or "one half dozen salts, Block Cut." Museums classified glass by motif: "Amphora, cut, Thumbprint" or "bowl, cut Flute."

Such easy descriptions of cut-glass designs prevailed until the conversion of the power serving the cutting house from steam to electricity. The higher speed of the electrically driven cutting wheel made possible intricate and involved combinations of old motifs. As competition between glass houses increased, manufacturers found more names for their patterns. Later (1880–1919) designers patented their designs with their titles.

Because more than two hundred cutting houses were in operation in America during the best years of the Brilliant Period, between 1880 and 1905—and because most of these either pirated established patterns, such as Russian Pillar, Strawberry-Diamond and Fan, and Corning, or invented variations of their own—a conservative estimate of patterns and variations for these years would be well over five hundred. Many of these were variations of standard patterns or were cut on single pieces only. Other patterns were cut in limited quantity so that they exist now only in musty, dog-eared catalogues.

The list of patterns that follows has been selected with reference to three criteria: availability, representative design, and intrinsic value.

A greater number of pieces were cut in these patterns, so more pieces survive for today's collectors.

The patterns are easily identified by reason of a dominant motif.

They are well balanced designs, examples of the best patterns of the period whose heirloom attributes make them investments of ever increasing value.

In most cases, if the collector first becomes familiar with the basic motifs of cut-glass patterns, the search for specific designs is not difficult.

Only for the purist is it necessary to have each fan detail, each cross-hatched partition and star identical on each piece. It is well to remember that cut glass, the product of a man's skill and trained talent, is individual in its production. Even with the cutting pattern before him, a cutter could make a mistake, add an individual embellishment, leave the mark of his personality on his work. Sometimes two pieces cut on the same pattern by the same cutter were not identical. Imperfections in the glass blank sometimes forced the cutter to cut around a chip or a "bleb."

By finding the dominant motif and working back from that, the pattern comes into focus, or the variant is discovered. Some collectors enjoy the pursuit of the variant, as in the case of the Russian pattern. Among others, there are Russian and Swirl, Russian and Flute, Russian and Hobnail, Russian and Hob Star, Russian and Fan, but the dominant Russian cutting is always there to unify the collection.

Other dominant motifs are Hobnail, Strawberry-Diamond (most frequently combined with Fan), Block, Chair Bottom, Flute, Notched Prism. The various star motifs range from the single star to the elaborate 32-point hob star and the later Pinwheel pattern.

The prices listed here are a composite, or average, of the present prevailing price tags on glass in a cross section of antique shops, shows, and old-glass markets in all parts of the United

States. It may be possible to buy any single piece listed for much less in some localities, or in some areas the asking prices may be twice as much. In antique glass, as in any other commodity, the rule of supply and demand is operative. If a punch bowl cut in the Russian pattern, in mint condition, can be had at a church bazaar for $125, happy day for the buyer. Such finds do not reflect a true market.

But also, the market in this year of Grace in no way reflects the true value of cut glass. Aside from Early-American cut glass —those exquisite examples of Bakewell and the early-nineteenth-century output of New England glass companies, and other pieces whose value is now reckoned only by the enchanted barter of knowledgeable collectors—American cut glass is being bought and sold today for a fraction of its real worth.

In 1950, Mr. Samuel Hawkes—son of the glass pioneer Thomas G. Hawkes, late of Waterford and founder of the T. G. Hawkes cutting house of Corning, New York—made a careful study of the cost of production of a ten-inch berry bowl cut in the Carolyn pattern at mid-twentieth-century labor and material costs. Sand, lead, and labor figured at the 1950 cost put the wholesale cost of reproduction of the bowl at a little more than $100. Yet the retail cost of such an antique bowl today is only about $50.

Russian-cut goblets engraved with the crest of the President of the United States were discontinued during the Franklin Delano Roosevelt administration when the cost soared to $750 per dozen, and a less expensive cutting was substituted for the White House State dining table.

In the ten years between 1950 and 1960, cost of materials and labor increased another 50 per cent. A conservative estimate of the replacement value of a compote cut in the Columbia pattern, listed here at $75, is $246, if, of course, any craftsman could be found with the skill to cut the intricate polished pillars in the pattern.

One last word of caution: When you buy cut glass, be certain that it is CUT. In the last half of the nineteenth century (after 1864), much lime glass was pressed to imitate cut glass. These pressed pieces, made in molds, lack the luster, weight, and sharpness of true cut glass.

Only glass containing lead is "soft" enough to be cut on or by a moving wheel. Open pieces, that is bowls or nappies, tumblers, goblets, and compotes, will ring when tapped lightly. The edges of the patterns on cut glass will feel keen to the touch.

Mold marks and bumps or raised ridges on the inside of bowls are sure signs that the pieces are not fine cut glass but premolded imitations. In these, the deeper incisions were pressed into the blank, then cut over on a wheel and fire-polished to give a false brilliance. These pieces lack the luster and sharpness of the true cut glass and are easily identified after a little practice. Their value is not a tenth of true cut-glass pieces.

The standards of quality in cut glass are weight, prismatic luster, and sharpness and precision in the wheel cutting. If these qualities are not inherent in the piece, it is an imitation no matter what its pattern and should be treated as a commercial item rather than a collector's treasure.

Occasionally, pieces of fine glass will show a small acid-etched trademark on the bottom of stemmed ware or in the base of bowls. This is a fine proof of manufacturer but it is not an indication of superior value. Few of the nineteenth-century pieces have such marks. The Thomas G. Hawkes Company and the Libbey Glass Company started the practice as a guarantee of quality but many fine Libbey pieces, as well as those of the Hawkes Company cut before 1895, have no such identification. The acid mark merely identifies the house and dates the piece as having been cut between 1892 and 1914. A number of houses used acid trademarks during those years. The very handsome early Brilliant Period cut glass has no marks.

Information and background have been kept at a minimum in the PRICE GUIDE TO AMERICAN CUT GLASS, since its purpose is to be a handbook for easy reference. But, because cut-glass values are steadily rising, it would be well for the collector to become thoroughly acquainted with the three periods of American cut glass—its development and its distinguishing characteristics of "color," shape, and motifs—by referring frequently to the author's *Cut & Engraved Glass—1771–1905.* References to this text are found in the PRICE GUIDE wherever specific additional information seemed relevant.

The PRICE GUIDE is meant to be just that. The fifty patterns listed are representative of the Brilliant Period and were selected to cover the entire period and for their diversity of pattern. Although no exact chronological order can be maintained, the patterns are shown in a sequence, beginning with motifs cut in the late nineteenth century (Strawberry-Diamond, Flute, Block) to those cut only in the later years of the period (Rosette, Pinwheel), that gives a logical progression of style.

It is surprising that, out of the tons and carloads of glass cut in the last years of the nineteenth century and the early years of this one, so relatively few pieces survive. But sudden temperature change, or extremes of heat or cold, fracture cut glass along the cutting fissures. Weight, caused by stacking, takes its toll, too, especially of plates and tumblers. Plates in any pattern are now extremely rare.

Not all the pieces listed in this guide can be found in any one locality. Some alas, are rare indeed. Nor will you necessarily find examples of precisely the patterns illustrated here. Each pattern, nevertheless, is typical of a wide range of similar cuttings, so that, by comparing motifs, arrangement of design, and style, a comparative price for almost any piece of glass cut between 1875 and 1920 may be established. Identifiable patterns do, however, command the premium price.

This is a guide to a treasure hunt, for every piece of cut glass you own or find is uniquely precious.

1. STRAWBERRY-DIAMOND

If you are looking for a collection of this pattern to be used on your table for special occasions, you may have to settle for variants, that is "like but not identical" cuttings. Strawberry-Diamond was a consistent favorite over as many as twenty years. It was found in all catalogues and was one of the less expensive patterns because of its simple, straight line cuttings.

Many of these pieces carry trademarks of T. G. Hawkes Company, Libbey Glass Company, and H. Hoare Company. Strawberry-Diamond was cut by many companies between 1890 and 1910.

Berry bowls	
6″	$10.00
7″	12.00
8″	15.00
9″	18.00
10″	25.00
Butter patty, 3″ stemmed	5.00
Celery dishes	
boat—flat, square	15.00
vase—straight or flared	25.00
Champagne jug, 2-quart	30.00
Claret jugs	
pint	25.00
quart	35.00

(Watch out for handles and stoppers. If handles are cracked at base, or stoppers are not original ones cut in pattern, the pieces have little value.)

Cologne bottles, all shapes	15.00
Compotes	
6″ and 7″	20.00
8″ and 10″	30.00
8″ and 10″, covered	50.00

1. STRAWBERRY-DIAMOND

Cream jugs—globe, straight	$10.00
Cruets, 6″ or 8″	15.00
Decanter, quart	35.00
(These should have original stoppers, be free of chips at neck, and naturally should not have cracks.)	
Finger bowl	10.00
Goblet (rare)	15.00
Nappies, all sizes	20.00
Plates, 6″, 8½″, 10″, 12″, 13″	15.00
Salts—globe, tub, square	5.00 ea.
Sauce dishes, 4½″ and 5″, no handles	15.00
Tumbler	5.00
Wine glass (all sizes)	5.00

Note: You may find additional pieces such as perfume bottles, pin trays, olive dishes, candleholders, etc. Prices on these specialty items are consistent with more available pieces as listed. No Strawberry-Diamond piece of good quality (good metal, sharp cutting, no cracks or chips) should sell for less than $5.00, regardless of size.

Variants: Strawberry-Diamond and Fan combines well with the standard pattern.

See *Cut & Engraved Glass*, Plate 95, page 227, pages 346–348, 350–352, and Index.

2. FLUTE

Many flute cuttings are to be found in decanters, pitchers, compotes, wine glasses, and cups. Plates are rarer.

There are two divisions of the Flute pattern separated by as many as fifty years in origin. The collector of Flute should first be familiar with "color." Older pieces, that is, Flute cutting from New England, Pittsburgh, and Schuylkill houses of the Early American period tend to be gray in color, "mellow,"

Plates

10″	$25.00
8″	20.00
6″	15.00
Tumbler	8.00

Wine glasses

Champagne	10.00
Claret	8.00
liquor	5.00
syllabub cup	10.00

Incidental pieces

pickle dish	10.00
small nappy	10.00
salt dish	5.00
celery vase (very rare)	100.00

See *Cut & Engraved Glass*, Plates 60, 61, 62, 63, pages 126–128, 130–132, 139–143, and Index.

3. HOBNAIL

The Hobnail motif is a 6-sided, flat-topped motif resembling the hobnail of a heavy boot.

The Hobnail was adopted by American cutters from old English and Irish cut glass. Many American houses after 1880 used the Hobnail as an over-all cutting distinctive of the Brilliant Period.

Care should be taken to distinguish cut pieces from pressed glass in the Hobnail motif. Cut pieces are heavy, edges of hobnails are sharp to the fingers. Cutting is deep and well defined. The Hobnail motif contributes to the prismatic sparkle of open pieces.

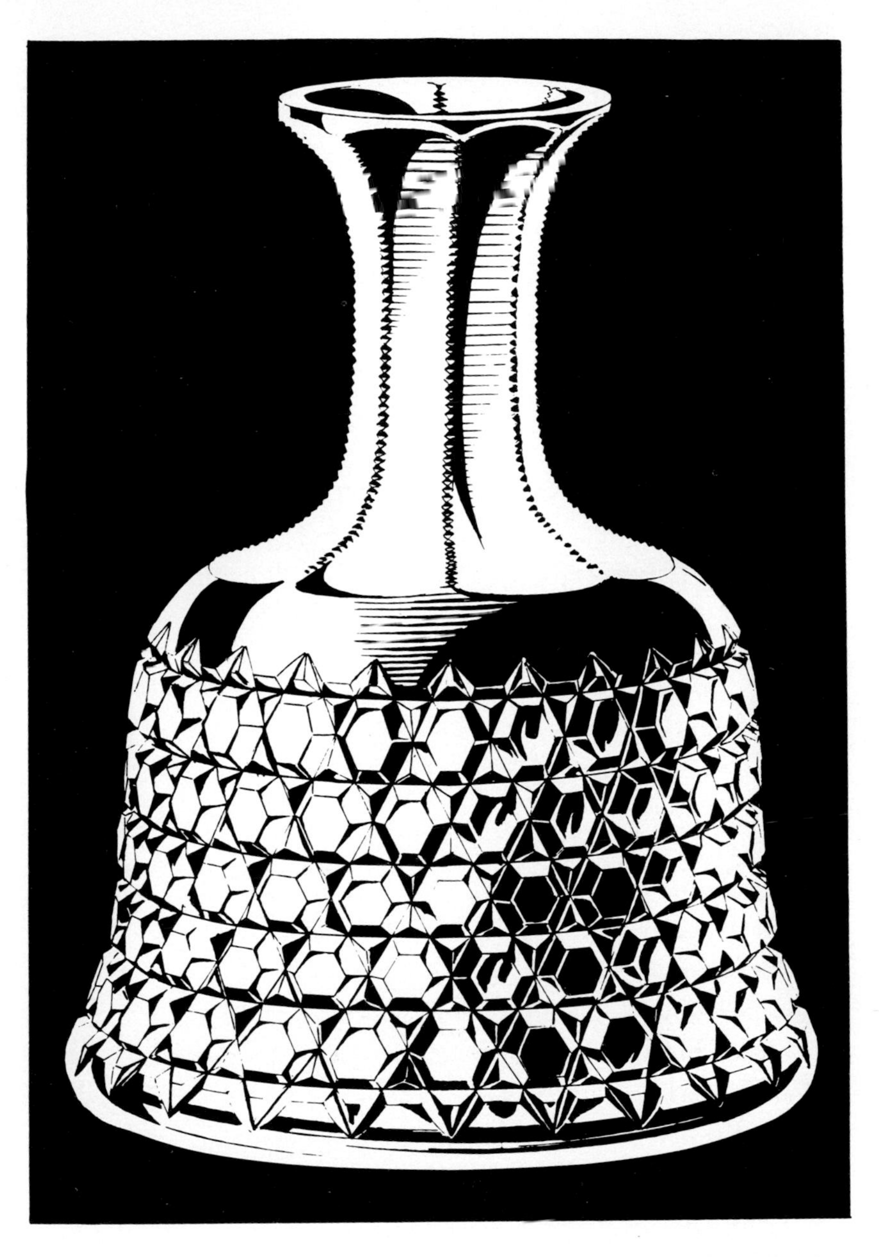

3. HOBNAIL

Bowls	
punch	$225.00
12″ stemmed fruit	65.00
12″ berry	50.00
10″ berry	35.00
8″ flat	25.00
11″ oblong nappy	30.00
5″ finger bowl, sugar bowl	10.00
Goblets and wine glasses	
goblet	10.00
tumbler	8.00
Sherry	5.00
Claret	5.00
cordial	5.00
Plates	
12″	25.00
10″	20.00
ice-cream platter	50.00
pin tray	10.00
Specialty pieces	
basket	25.00
bonbon or olive dish	20.00
butter patty	5.00
celery vase	35.00
mustard jar	10.00
butter bowl and plate	25.00
rose bowl	20.00
candlesticks	15.00 ea.
toothpick holder	10.00
vases (depending on size)	20.00 to 50.00
Pitchers	
globe	35.00
Champagne	40.00
straight	30.00
syrup	25.00
cream	20.00

Cologne bottle	$25.00
Decanter	45.00
Cruet	20.00
Smelling salts	15.00

Variations combine cross-hatching of hobnail in strawberry cutting; partitions with fan and flute.

For illustration of Hobnail decanter with notched flute neck, see *Cut & Engraved Glass*, page 153, Plate 67. See also pages 206–209.

4. BLOCK MOTIF

A Block motif may be either square or rectangular. One of the oldest cut-glass motifs, it is sometimes called the Irish Block.

The motif was used in all three periods of glass cutting. Colonial or Early American pieces are for the most part simple in design, the metal "mellow" in color, softer in appearance.

All patterns in which the Block motif is dominant combine well together in a collection. Block-motif patterns are not as numerous as either Strawberry-Diamond or Bull's-Eye. For that reason their prices are generally higher:

Bowls

10″ berry	$45.00
8″ nappy	35.00
8″ rose	30.00
punch	250.00

(Be sure it is cut. Pressed punch bowls were made in this pattern.)

Butter patty	10.00
Candlesticks	25.00 ea.
Celery boat	35.00
Champagne jug	50.00
Cheese dish with cover	45.00
Claret jug	45.00

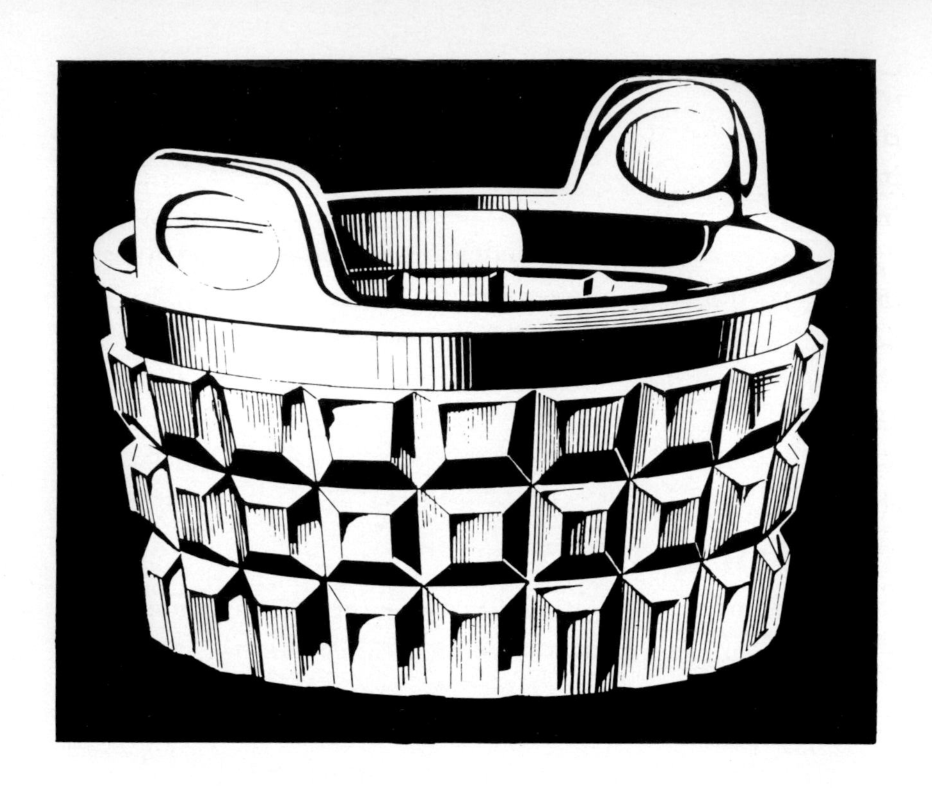

4. BLOCK MOTIF

Cologne bottles	
square	$20.00
globe	25.00
Compotes	
12″ stemmed	50.00
8″ stemmed	25.00
Decanter, square	50.00
Finger bowl	25.00
Goblet	15.00
Plate	25.00
Salt, square	15.00
Spoon holder	25.00
Toothpick holder	15.00
Wine-glass washer (butter tub)	25.00

See *Cut & Engraved Glass*, pages 181–183, and Index.

5. BULL'S-EYE

Bull's-Eye is the American term for the concave ball motif used in cut-glass design since before the fourth century, B.C. Known in various countries and in different centuries as a "roundelet," "puntie," "printie," or "Kugle," it has been used either alone or in combination with other motifs in all periods of cut-glass design.

Collections featuring the Bull's-Eye as a dominant motif will cross the lines of periods including Early American pieces, Middle Period glass, and Brilliant cutting. In all patterns included in such a collection, the Bull's-Eye should be dominant.

The Thumbprint, which is simply an elongated ball motif, may also be included in a collection of Bull's-Eye patterns.

Bonbon or olive dishes	
square	$35.00
round	25.00
Bowls	
7″ berry	20.00
8″ berry	25.00
9″ berry	30.00
10″ berry	35.00
punch	250.00
Butter patty	5.00
Celery dishes	
boat	20.00
vase	35.00
Champagne pitcher	40.00
Claret jug	45.00
Cologne bottles	
globe	20.00
square	25.00
tapered	20.00
Compotes	
7″ with tall foot	35.00
6″ covered, stemmed	30.00

5. BULL'S-EYE

Cream pitcher	$25.00
Cruet	20.00
Decanter	45.00
Finger bowl	10.00
Goblet	10.00
Nappies	
7″ square or oblong	20.00
8″ round or oblong	25.00
9″ round or oval	30.00
Pitchers	
1-quart straight	40.00
2-quart globe	45.00
Plates	
6″ single motif	30.00
8″ Bull's-Eye in combination	35.00
10″ Bull's-Eye or Thumbprint in combination	40.00
Sauce dish	20.00
Sugar bowl	25.00
Toothpick holder	15.00
Tumbler	10.00
Wine glass (all sizes)	10.00

The Bull's-Eye motif, plain or in combination with others, was cut by many cutting shops during the nineteenth century.

See *Cut & Engraved Glass,* pages 161, 276, 289, 291.

6. RUSSIAN

A combination of the star and Hobnail, the Russian pattern was patented in 1882 by Philip McDonald, a cutter for Thomas G. Hawkes Company of Corning, New York. Soon after, a complete service in this pattern was cut by Hawkes for the Russian Embassy in Washington, D.C. In 1885, another service was cut for the American Embassy in St. Petersburg and the pattern became known as the Russian.

6. RUSSIAN

An elaborate all-over pattern, it was immensely popular in the late nineteenth century, and variations were cut by many of the better glass houses. An expensive pattern, it was highly prized, particularly in goblets, tumblers, and wine glasses.

Unhappily, though well-known and easily recognized, it is now rare, because intricate and heavy cutting makes the glass unusually subject to temperature and pressure fracture. The Russian pattern is now so rare that pieces should be treated only as units in a "cabinet" collection. Exceptions are decanters and cologne bottles. Goblets, tumblers, and plates are particularly subject to fracture.

Prices listed are for Russian pattern or for predominant Russian motif in combination variants, such as Russian and Swirl,

Russian and Star, Russian and Flute. Any Russian piece that bears the engraving of the Great Seal of the United States is worth five times the price listed below.

Care should be taken to distinguish between the Russian, a cut pattern, and the pressed-glass Daisy and Button, a pressed copy. The usual tests apply. In the Russian cut pieces, the glass is heavy, brighter, prismatic, open pieces ring, and edges of cut patterns are keen to the touch, sometimes even sharp.

Basket	$125.00
Bonbon or olive dishes	
5″ or 6″ round	20.00
5″ crescent	25.00
6″ leaf	25.00
Bowls	
7″ flat-bottom	45.00
8″ square	50.00
9″ round	55.00
10″ oval	60.00
12″ berry	75.00
Bread plate	50.00
Butter dish	15.00
Butter tub with plate	45.00
Candlesticks	30.00 ea.
Celery dishes	
boat	45.00
vase	50.00
Champagne jug	100.00
Claret jug	125.00
Cocktail glass	15.00
Cologne bottle	50.00
Compotes	
8″ short-stemmed	50.00
9″ medium-stemmed	60.00
10″ medium-stemmed	75.00
Cruet	25.00

Decanters	
pint	$50.00
pint and a half	65.00
quart	75.00
globe	75.00
ring-necked	100.00
Finger bowl	30.00
Goblet	25.00
Highball	30.00
Ice-cream platter (very rare)	250.00
Mustard jar	35.00
Nappies	
7″, 8″, 9″ square	40.00
7″, 8″, 9″, 10″, 12″ round	45.00
6″ × 9″ oblong	45.00
Pin tray	25.00
Plate	40.00
Powder box	45.00
Punch bowl	550.00
Punch cup	25.00
Salts—globe, square, tub	15.00 ea.
Sauce dish	20.00
Sherbet cup	25.00
Smelling salts	25.00
Spoon holder	25.00
Sugar bowl	40.00
Syrup pitcher	35.00
Toothpick holders—square, round, flat, stemmed	25.00
Tumbler	25.00
Vases—tall, straight, stemmed	35.00
Water pitcher	50.00
Wine glasses	
Champagne, Claret, cordial	15.00
hock, Madeira, Sherry	18.00

See *Cut & Engraved Glass*, pages 182–185, and Index.

7. NOTCHED PRISM

This is a turn-of-the-century pattern but one that is easy to assemble because of the many variations in the general prism-design theme.

The metal is usually heavy and the forms are Victorian. The prism motif with variations of notching was used particularly on pieces of singular elegance such as vases, bowls, and punch bowls. Tumblers and goblets are rare.

One fascinating possibility in collecting Notched-Prism pattern variants is the chance of finding a green or red or blue overlay cut through in notches. Prices for colored cut glass are given at the end of the list for crystal Notched-Prism pieces.

Bonbon or olive dish	$15.00
Bowls	
4½″	10.00
8″	20.00
Butter plate	5.00
Cheese plate with cover	35.00
Celery dishes	
boat	25.00
vase	40.00
Cologne bottles	
narrow-necked	20.00
globe	25.00
Compotes	
7″ stem	30.00
10″ stem	40.00
Cruet	25.00
Decanters	
Rodney	35.00
globe	40.00
Goblets	
tapering	20.00
standard	25.00

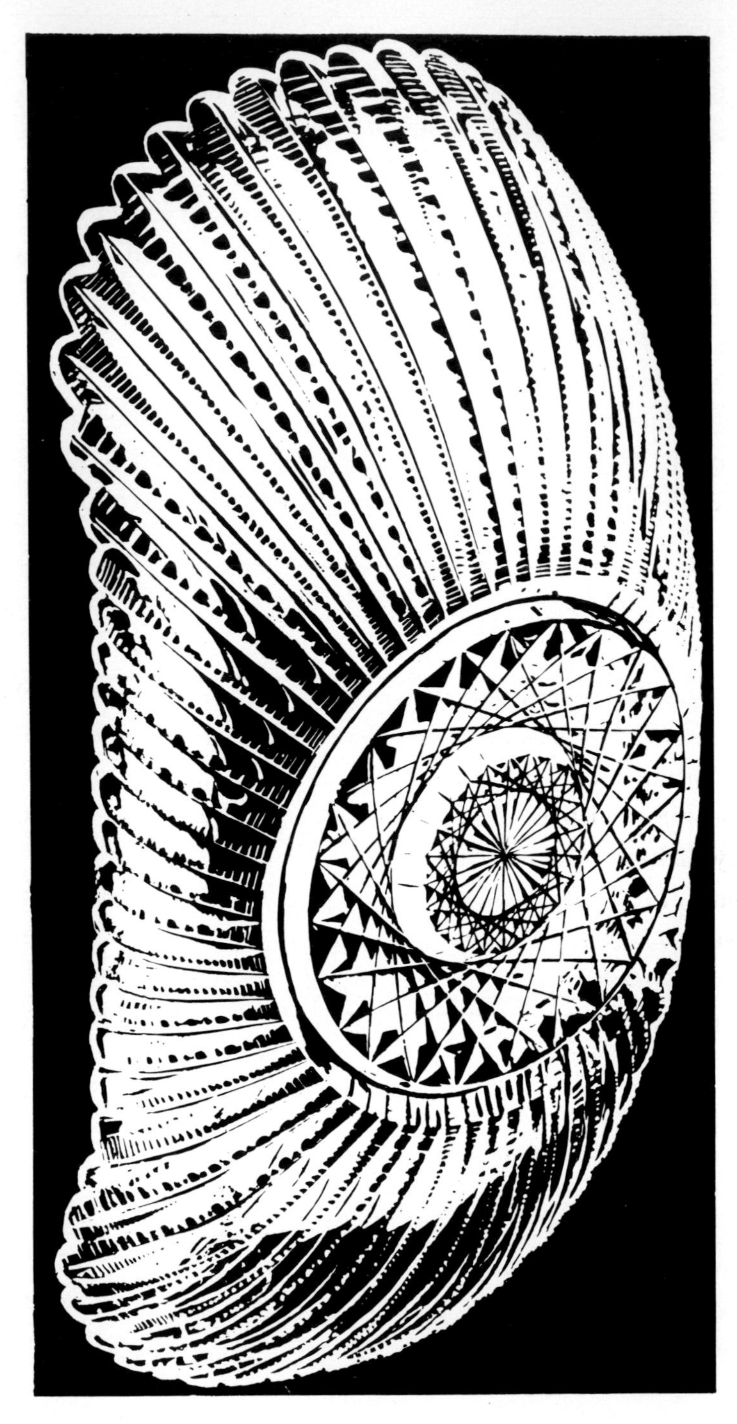

7. NOTCHED PRISM

Nappies

7″ round	$25.00
8″ square	30.00
9″ oblong	35.00
10″ round shallow	40.00
Pitcher, straight-sided, one-quart	50.00

Plates (rare)

6″	20.00
8″	30.00
10″	35.00
12″	45.00
Punch bowl	400.00
Rose bowl	25.00
Salts	10.00 ea.
Sauce dish	15.00
Sherbet cup	20.00
Sugar bowl	35.00
Syrup pitcher	30.00
Tumbler	20.00
Vases (these come in a variety of shapes and sizes. Price varies with size, metal, shape, and cutting.)	20.00 to 75.00
Wine glass	15.00

For variants of Prism patterns, see *Cut & Engraved Glass*, Pattern 38, Prism, page 274; Pattern 39, White House, page 276; Pattern 44, Bull's-Eye (with Prism detail), page 289. See also pages 164–167, 181–183.

Colored-overlay Notched Prism

Cologne (green, red)	$45.00
Decanter (green, red, blue)	65.00
Goblet (green, red)	35.00

9. GLADYS

9. GLADYS

A late-nineteenth-century pattern (1885), cut principally by T. G. Hawkes and Christian Dorflinger, it had great success as a design for cut tableware. The pattern is one of especial elegance. The 8-point star fits neatly in a design using a fan at the top, and a partitioned triangle is cross-hatched.

When looking for this pattern, search for the 8-point star as the focal motif. There are other 8-point-star and fan patterns that combine with Gladys in a collection, but the true example of the pattern will show the cross-hatched supporting triangle.

Bonbon or olive dishes	
7″ flat	$20.00
7″ with handle	25.00
Bowls	
8″ berry	25.00
10″ berry	45.00
Celery boat	40.00
Compote	50.00
Cruets	
6″ straight	20.00
8″ globe	30.00
Goblet	20.00
Nappy	35.00
Pitcher	50.00
Plate	38.00
Sauce dish	20.00
Salts	15.00 ea.
Tumbler	20.00
Wine glass	15.00

10. COLUMBIA

The "elephant-tusk" motifs are the distinguishing characteristic of the Columbia pattern (1893). Designed by Libbey to be featured at the Columbian Exposition in Chicago, it was a highly successful pattern and was cut in color as well as crystal.

The "tusks" are in pillar-smooth cutting. These, combined with the 20-point star and cross-hatched supporting areas at the base, make a distinguished design. The Columbia is one of the first patterns to use the 20-point star as a central motif.

Berry bowl, 9″	$25.00
Butter dish with cover	45.00
Celery vase	40.00
Cheese dish with cover	35.00
Cologne bottles	
4-ounce, square	20.00
6″ × 6″ globe	25.00
8″ globe	30.00
Compotes	
10″ bowl	75.00
6″ pedestal	75.00
Cream pitcher, globe	35.00
Cruets	
6-ounce	20.00
8-ounce, with handle	25.00
Decanter	50.00
Dish, 4″, odd shapes	20.00
Finger bowl	25.00
Goblet (rare)	30.00
Nappies	
7″	20.00
8″	25.00
9″	30.00
Pitchers	
round	45.00
globe	50.00

10. COLUMBIA

11. CORNING

Plates	
6″	$35.00
10″	40.00
Salts	
globe	15.00
table	20.00
Sherbet cup	20.00
Spoon holder, straight	25.00
Punch cup	15.00
Tumbler	15.00
Wine glass	15.00

Colored Pieces

Cologne bottle with green overlay	45.00
Finger bowl with red overlay	35.00

See *Cut & Engraved Glass*, pages 248–251.

11. CORNING

The Corning pattern may have been cut before 1895 but does not appear in catalogues before that date. Corning was originally cut by the J. B. Hoare Company of Corning, New York, on blanks made at the Corning Glass Works. It was a very popular pattern in the closing years of the nineteenth century.

Corning is an attractive partition arrangement of straight splits which, when cut in a border, form small squares decorated with small single or button stars and larger squares in which a 16-point hob star is centered. This geometric partitioning of the pattern with the hob star being "contained" is typical of cut designs of the late nineteenth century.

Berry bowls	
7″ flat	$25.00
8″ round	30.00
9″ small foot	35.00
10″ square	40.00

Butter dish and cover	$35.00
Butter patty	10.00
Candlesticks	25.00 ea.
Celery dishes	
vase	30.00
square	35.00
Center bowl	50.00
Champagne jug	45.00
Cheese dish and cover	35.00
Claret jug and stopper	39.00
Cologne bottle	27.00
Cream jug	26.00
Decanter	32.00
Finger bowl	17.00
Goblet	15.00
Plates	
7–8″ square	25.00
8–9″ round	20.00
Punch bowl	450.00
Rose bowl	15.00
Salts	5.00 ea.
Spoon holder	8.00
Sugar bowl	25.00
Syrup pitcher	29.00
Toothpick holder	10.00
Tumbler	12.00
Wine glass	10.00

The Oriental pattern and the Meteor are variations which combine well with Corning. The Cleary is similar.

See *Cut & Engraved Glass,* Plate 109, and pages 259–261, 263.

12. CROESUS

One of the earliest patterns to use the chair-bottom motif, Croesus was very popular in the late nineteenth century. The

12. CROESUS

glass was blown at the Corning Glass Works and cut by the J. Hoare Company. Distinctive in the combination of fans with the chair-bottom squares are graceful curved splits above swirled pillars with notched prisms accentuating the rhythm of the design. The effect is unified and graceful.

It is an expensive pattern, but one that makes a beautiful contribution to a collection of nineteenth-century cut-glass pieces.

Berry bowls	
7″ shallow	$38.00
8″ footed	42.00
9″ square	45.00
10″ round	50.00
Bonbon or olive dishes	
5″ and 6″ round	25.00
Carafe, quart	50.00
Nappy, 14″ × 8″ oval	42.00
Punch bowls	
10″ high with pedestal, 20″ × 13″ oval	425.00
Punch cup with handle	18.00
Sauce dishes, 4″ and 4½″ shallow	15.00
Wine glasses, all sizes	12.00

See *Cut & Engraved Glass,* pages 262–263, and Index.

13. ZENDA

An interesting and simple pattern cut by many houses over a period of thirty years, Zenda is a combination of deep fans and alternate triangles of cross-hatching and Strawberry-Diamond. It was not as expensive a pattern to cut as some of the more intricate later star patterns, and it was popular in a variety of decanters, tumblers, and goblets.

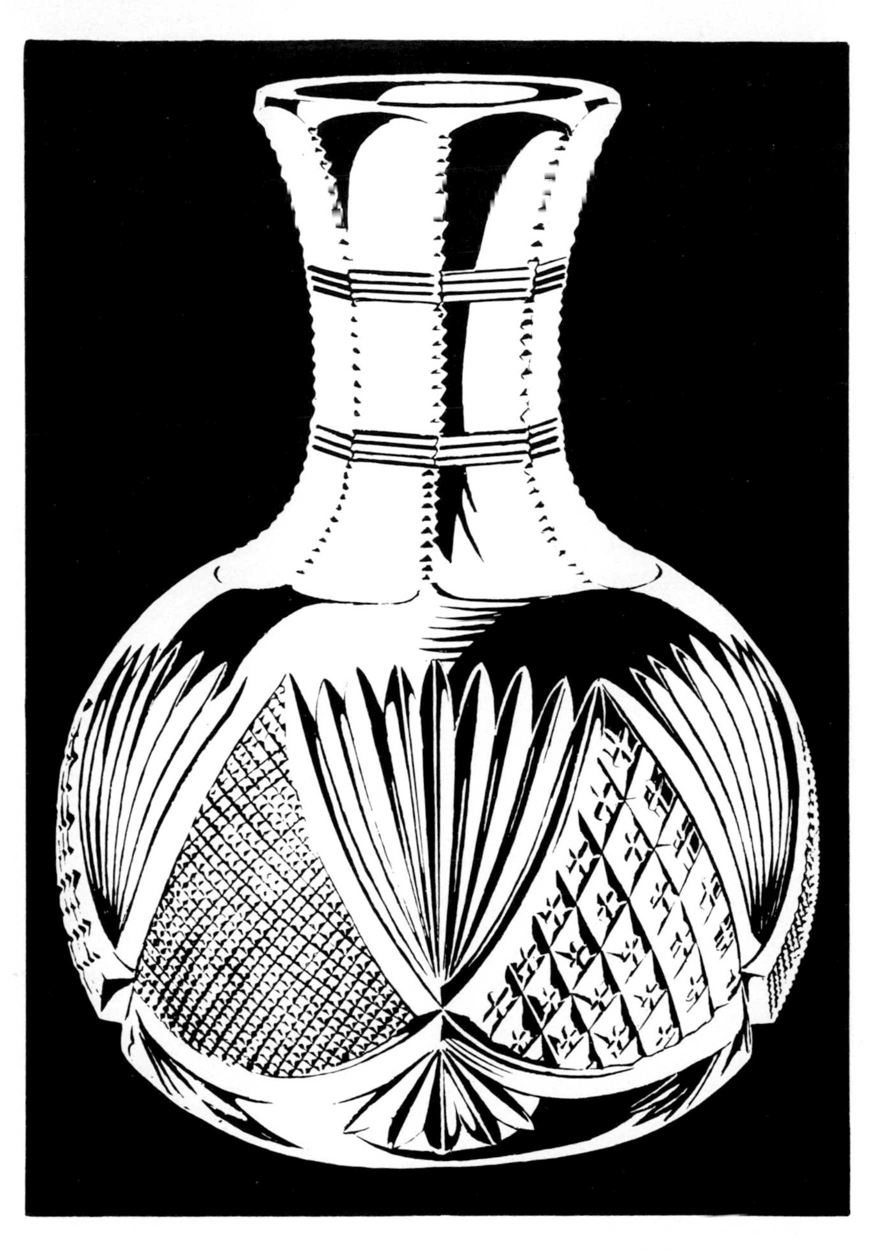

13. ZENDA

Berry bowls	
7″, 8″, 9″ flat-bottom	$30.00
10″ with foot	45.00
Bonbon dish, covered	20.00
Butter patty	5.00
Candlesticks	20.00 ea.
Carafe	30.00
Celery boat	25.00
Center bowl	40.00
Champagne jug	42.00
Cologne bottle, 6-ounce globe	15.00
Cruets	
8″ globe	20.00
6″ (oil)	18.00
Decanters	
narrow-necked	35.00
cordial	21.00
Finger bowl	18.00
Goblet	10.00
Pitchers	
globe	25.00
straight	28.00
Plates	
6″ and 8″ round	30.00
10″ and 12″ square or oval (rare)	35.00
Punch bowl	350.00
Punch cup	10.00
Salts	12.00 ea.
Sauce dish	15.00
Sherbet cup	12.00
Spoon holder	18.00
Toothpick holder	10.00
Tumbler	12.00

Vases, depending on size, from

globe	$25.00
rose	up to 125.00
Wine glass	10.00

14. REGAL

Another of the chair-bottom or rattan patterns, Regal was cut in the 1880s when craftsmen had time to work in elaborate splits not unlike the swag cuttings of a century earlier. Regal has curving bands of chair bottom and cross-hatching accenting square motifs of chair bottom, with fans for pointing up the intersections of the curving borders.

A well-designed pattern, it has simple elegance and is assuredly one of the earlier patterns of the Brilliant Period. The pieces usually have straight sides.

Berry bowl, 10″	$42.00
Butter patty, 3″, flat	10.00
Candlesticks	20.00 ea.
Carafe	45.00
Celery dish, oblong	35.00
Center bowl, 12″ (rare)	60.00
Cologne bottle, globe	20.00
Cruet, 6-ounce, with handle	25.00
Decanters	
quart, globe	50.00
tapering	42.00
cordial	22.00
Finger bowl	20.00
Goblet (rare)	18.00
Pitcher, globe, with handle	55.00

14. REGAL

Plates

6″ (rare)	$20.00
10″ (rare)	43.00

Punch bowl with pedestal	185.00
Punch cup with handle	15.00
Sugar bowl	28.00
Tumbler	20.00
Vases	20.00 to 125.00
Wine glass	15.00

15. MONARCH

One of the first of the hob-star patterns, Monarch was cut in the late nineteenth century and continued to be popular during the early twentieth-century fashion for more flamboyant cutting.

It has a 24-point hob star contained in a square formed by deep miter splits. The joining figure is an ellipse with smaller star balanced by a cross-hatched area. The pattern is accented by fans which co-ordinate the square of the star to the ellipse. The features of the pattern to look for are the hob star in the square and the elliptical joining figure. Variants will have diverse cuttings in this ellipse. All have the fans.

Bowls

pedestal	$80.00
punch	420.00
7″	35.00
10″ flat	50.00
12″	65.00

Celery boat	37.00
Cologne	32.00

15. MONARCH

Compote	$62.00
Cup	15.00
Decanters	
quart	52.00
pint	40.00
with handle	48.00
Finger bowl	15.00
Goblet	20.00
Plate	37.00
Salts	12.00 ea.
Sauce dish	18.00
Tumbler	15.00
Vases, depending on size and shape	15.00 to 60.00
Wine glass	17.00

16. SIGNORA

Here is a pattern in which many bowls, bottles, and tumblers were cut by many houses from about 1903. It is a compact design of a 16-point star contained in a square composed of double rows of small notched flutes with single stars in the corners. The inevitable fan, this one well defined with "leaves," ties the pattern together at top and base.

Baskets	
12″	$60.00
6″	35.00
Bonbon or olive dish	20.00
Bowls, 7″, 8″, 10″	80.00
Candlesticks	30.00 ea.
Celery boat	40.00
Claret jug	65.00
Cologne bottle, globe or tapering	30.00
Compote	85.00

16. SIGNORA

Cruet, globe or straight	$30.00
Decanters	
quart	62.00
pint	48.00
Finger bowl	25.00
Goblet	20.00
Nappy	45.00
Pitcher	64.00
Plate (rare)	85.00
Punch bowl	575.00

Sauce dish	$22.00
Sugar bowl	28.00
Tumbler	18.00
Wine glass	15.00

7. X-RAY

X-Ray is one of the easier patterns to identify. The basic element of the design is a large 16-point hob star surrounded by smaller rectangular and triangular fields of cross-hatching. The distinguishing elements of the pattern are the "rays" which radiate from between the points of the star like beams.

On the bottoms of the larger bowls, the points of the star (now a 24-point star) show cross-hatching between the points. The rectangular areas of cross-hatching are slashed to give the appearance of a beam of light. Bowls have scalloped tops. The decanters and colognes are finished at the top by rows of diagonal half flutes. A very beautiful pattern, cut between 1895 and 1910.

Bonbon or olive dish	$15.00
Bowls	
7″	27.00
8″	31.00
10″	39.00
Butter dish with cover	37.00
Celery dishes	
boat	32.00
vase	37.00
Champagne pitcher	42.00
Cologne bottle	22.00
Compote	47.00
Cream pitcher	22.00

17. X-RAY

Cruet	$18.00
Cup	20.00
Decanter	44.00
Finger bowl	20.00
Goblet	15.00
Nappy	28.00
Pitcher	37.00
Plate	32.00

Punch bowl	$325.00
Sauce dish	18.00
Tumbler	15.00
Wine glass	12.00

18. TOKIO

This is a band pattern as contrasted with the over-all designs. Tokio will show a well-defined 24-point star on the bottoms of bowls, nappies, and open pieces, but the dominant pattern is a band made up of 4-part motifs separated by fans. The 4-partition motif, which is not precisely a square, is topped by a simple 8-point hob star. The two matching sections are cross-hatched. The lower section is an inverted fan.

Although the Tokio is an attractive and orderly pattern, it was never one of the more expensive ones and so was widely cut (between 1895 and 1910) and is collectible in a wide range of pieces.

Bowls	
6″	$29.00
8″	32.00
9″	40.00
Box, oblong	30.00
Carafe	50.00
Celery dish	35.00
Cologne bottle	28.00
Compote	38.00
Cordial jug	35.00
Cruet	35.00
Cup	28.00
Decanter	48.00

18. TOKIO

Nappy (any size) $32.00
Pitcher 52.00
Plate 75.00
Punch bowl 420.00
Sauce bowl 42.00
Tumbler 21.00
Vases of all shapes ....20.00 to 75.00
Wine glass 20.00

19. DELFT

Care should be taken not to confuse this with Tokio. The motifs in Delft are square, but they alternate a large, square Strawberry-Diamond field with a broken field in which two stars are balanced by cross-hatching. Small fans unify the design. It will be noted here that the pattern is not as compact as Tokio, and the miter splits which form the squares carry on to form triangle areas which are left clear.

Bonbon dishes
 plain $20.00
 with handles 22.00
Bowl (all sizes) 32.00
Celery dish 28.00
Cologne bottle 32.00
Cruet 25.00
Cup 18.00
Decanter (all sizes) 45.00
Finger bowl 25.00
Nappy 36.00
Pitcher 42.00

19. DELFT

Plate (all sizes, rare)	$55.00
Punch bowl	450.00
Sauce dish	25.00
Tumbler	20.00
Wine glass	15.00

20. CAROLYN

This is a clean, concise pattern, easily identified because of the curving bands of chair-bottom motif framing a 20-point hob star. Fans top and bottom accent the design.

This pattern was widely cut by many houses in the early years of the twentieth century (1905–1909) and each manufacturer cut his own variant. Some have interesting bands of cross-hatching with the chair-bottom motifs. Early Carolyn pieces, however, are simple combinations of the star and curved chair bottom with fan, with no cross-hatching.

Berry bowls	
7″	$35.00
10″	50.00
Butter dish covered (with plate)	40.00
Butter patty	10.00
Celery dishes	
vase	38.00
dish	29.00
Center bowl, flat	65.00
Cologne bottles	
globe	25.00
straight	30.00
Compotes	
7″	55.00
10″	75.00

20. CAROLYN

Cream pitcher	$28.00
Cup (sherbet or punch)	18.00
Decanters	
globe	85.00
tapering	42.00
square	45.00
Finger bowl	22.00
Goblet	20.00
Olive dish	23.00
Plate (rare)	62.00
Punch bowl	445.00
Salts	15.00 ea.
Sugar bowl	35.00
Tumbler	22.00
Vases, depending on size	20.00 to 75.00
Wine glass	20.00

21. ELEANOR

Although this pattern was cut some time later than Carolyn, it is listed here for quick comparison. Often confused with the earlier pattern, Eleanor is a design of special elegance, combining the bands of chair-bottom motif with the 16-point (sometimes 20- or 24-point) stars set in well-defined points, alternating with partitioned points of cross-hatching. Eleanor was widely used as a design for punch bowls.

Bonbon dish	$20.00
Bowls	
7″	35.00
10″	45.00

21. ELEANOR

Celery boat	$28.00
Compote	42.00
Cruet	35.00
Cup	20.00
Goblet	20.00
Nappy	32.00
Pickle dish	35.00
Pitchers	
cream	30.00
water	52.00
Plate (rare)	62.00
Punch bowl	525.00
Salt dishes	18.00
Sauce dish	25.00
Sugar bowl, with cover	36.00
Tumbler	20.00
Wine glass	18.00

22. TASSO

Easily identified by its notched prisms and concentric squares, Tasso is one of the popular turn-of-the-century patterns. It uses a single star only, in the center of squares. The bowls and decanters in Tasso have a special brilliance because of the notched-prism cutting. Similar patterns are Hindoo and Pluto, combinations of notched prism and other small motifs.

An unusual pattern, it is highly prized, particularly in tumblers.

Bonbon dish	$28.00
Bowls	
6″ round	25.00
10″ round	40.00
12″ square	60.00

22. TASSO

Box, with cover	$35.00
Celery dishes	
vase	40.00
boat	32.00
Cologne	35.00
Cruet	32.00
Cup	20.00
Decanter	45.00
Goblet	25.00
Pitchers	
cream	30.00
water	55.00
Plate	40.00
Platter	65.00
Punch bowl	475.00
Salt dishes (nut dishes)	20.00 ea.
Sugar bowl	35.00
Tumbler	15.00
Wine glass	12.00

23. PEBBLE

Pebble cuttings in great variety were popular in the late nineteenth century. While the motif is similar to Strawberry-Diamond, the design is at right angles to the base. Libbey Glass Company cut many pieces of this design, with partitioned flutes separating the fields (1885).

Later, many glass houses combined the Pebble motif with 32-point stars or with swirled pillars to form variants of Libbey's Pebble. Some Pebble cuttings use the sharper nail-head diamonds in the pattern. Generally the title is descriptive of the appearance.

23. PEBBLE

Bonbon dish	$20.00
Bowls	
8″ square	30.00
10″ square	40.00
10″ round	35.00
Candlesticks	30.00 ea.
Celery boat	35.00
Cologne bottles	
globe	32.00
square	36.00
Compote	42.00
Cruet	35.00
Cup	18.00
Decanters	
pint	32.00
quart	45.00
Finger bowl	22.00
Goblet	20.00
Pitcher	48.00
Plate (rare)	52.00
Punch bowl	425.00
Sugar bowl with cover	48.00
Tumbler	75.00
Wine glass	18.00

24. SNOWFLAKE

Snowflake is a most attractive over-all design combining 8-point stars with cross-hatching and chair bottom, with fan, in small areas of the pattern made by an intricate intersection of miter splits. The central octagonal heart of each section is left clear, giving a distinguishing character to the pattern. This one is rare and was cut between 1895 and 1908.

24. SNOWFLAKE

Bowls	
10″ straight sides	$65.00
6″ straight sides	30.00
8″ round	52.00
Celery dish	55.00
Cologne	45.00
Compote	84.00
Cruet	48.00
Cup	30.00
Decanter, all types	75.00
Goblet	38.00
Pitcher	100.00
Plate	90.00
Punch bowl	650.00
Tumbler	32.00
Wine glass	28.00

25. HARVARD

A particularly handsome pattern, Harvard was widely cut in nappies, celery boats, and bowls. One of the over-all designs, the principal motif resembles a hobnail except that its surface is cut with a single star. In the Hawkes and Libbey pieces, the cutting is unusually sharp.

Originating in the cutting room of T. G. Hawkes, Harvard was cut from 1880 to the end of the Brilliant Period and was widely copied in many variations. This pattern should not be confused with the Russian pattern. In the Harvard, the motifs are clearly set apart from one another, usually by two parallel straight lines.

The Harvard pattern was cut by other companies with three dividing lines separating the motifs, under the pattern name of Kohinoor. The similarity is so great that the two may easily be combined in the same collection. A similar pattern, with a single dividing line and with square rather than round star-cut motifs, is Trellis.

Bonbon dish	$15.00
Bowls	
4½″	20.00
6″ flat	25.00
8″ round	35.00
10″ round	42.00
12″ round	50.00
Butter plate	18.00
Celery dishes	
boat	35.00
vase	43.00
Colognes	
square	28.00
globe	30.00
Compote	65.00
Cruet	38.00

25. HARVARD (Drawing adapted from a scrapbook of the T.G. Hawkes Glass Company)

Decanter	$52.00
Goblet	20.00
Nappy	37.00
Pitcher	64.00
Plate	48.00
Punch bowl	575.00
Salts	22.00 ea.
Sauce dish	30.00
Sugar bowl	42.00
Tumbler	20.00
Vases, depending on size	30.00 to 70.00
Wine glass	22.00

See *Cut & Engraved Glass*, pages 269–272.

26. RICHELIEU

Here is a pattern that is truly transitional. Older than most nineteenth-century cutting, it combines the curving flutes of the Middle Period of American cut glass with the elegance of the Brilliant Period that followed.

A bottom row of square motifs cut with an extended hobnail is connected by swirling flutes to a similar row at the top of the design. Very successful on bottles, jugs, colognes, and decanters, the motif was also widely cut on bowls, compotes, and pieces in which sufficient elevation gave grace to the swirling flutes. Cut by many houses under various names, in variants, Richelieu is a proud nineteenth-century pattern and relatively rare.

Bowls	
8″	$42.00
9″	45.00
10″ square	50.00
10″ round	48.00
Box	35.00
Carafe	42.00

27. OXFORD (Drawing adapted from an illustration in the files of the Libbey Glass Company)

Oxford is a geometric cutting in which the center row of squares contains hob stars separated from the top and bottom rows of hobnail squares by neat rectangles of cross-hatching. The Oxford is completed top and bottom by fans. A particularly attractive pattern on bowls, tumblers, and decanters.

Baskets	$45.00
Bowls	
6″	20.00
8″	25.00
10″	30.00
12″ square	42.00
Box	30.00
Catsup bottle	32.00
Celery dish	35.00
Cologne bottle (all shapes)	40.00
Compotes	
8″	52.00
10″	60.00
Cruet	35.00
Cup	20.00
Decanter	48.00
Goblet	28.00
Nappies	
6″ jelly dish	22.00
8″ preserves dish	28.00
Pickle dish (pedestal)	32.00
Pitcher	58.00
Plate	62.00
Punch bowl	525.00
Sauce dish	22.00
Sherbet cup	18.00
Tumbler	25.00
Vases, depending on size	35.00 to 150.00
Wine glass	20.00

28. NASSAU

Here is a quaint Victorian pattern that foreshadows the much later intaglio cuttings.

Nassau was widely cut in a number of variations and is collectible in many types of pieces. The distinguishing characteristic is the startlingly realistic daisy with stem, leaves, and bud, enclosed in a frame of double chair-bottom cutting. Some well-rounded bowls have a secondary motif of palm fronds or seeds near the top. A distinguished pattern and an old one (1886), Nassau was cut on intriguing shapes in keeping with its Victorian design.

Be sure to note that there were, before and later, intaglio cuttings of daisies in cut-glass design. Nassau has the chair-bottom frame, sometimes with a star in the corner. Without the chair-bottom frame, the design is not Nassau. Some pieces have added bands of partitioned squares across bottom or sides. These are also true Nassau pieces.

Baskets	
12″ tall	$35.00
10″ round with handles	32.00
Bonbon dish	23.00
Bowls	
6″	25.00
8″	28.00
9″	30.00
10″	32.00
8″ square	35.00
Catsup bottle	28.00
Celery dish	30.00
Cheese dish with cover	45.00
Cologne bottle	38.00
Compote	38.00
Cordial jug	40.00

28. NASSAU

Cruet	$33.00
Cup	20.00
Decanter	55.00
Goblet	20.00
Ice bucket	62.00
Jelly dish	23.00
Jug	39.00
Nappies	
6″	34.00
8″	38.00

Pickle dishes

stemmed	$37.00
oblong	33.00
Plate	69.00
Punch bowl	385.00
Sauce boat	34.00
Tumbler	22.00
Wine glass	20.00

29. WHEAT

There are several patterns by this name. Some use a swirled, notched flute terminating in a fan to resemble the beards of waving wheat. The Wheat patterns cut by the H. C. Fry Company and Libbey are of clear metal and cut on particularly attractive blanks (see *Cut & Engraved Glass*, page 177, Plate 75).

We show an older pattern here because it was cut more extensively and because it was for years the standard. Not all Wheat pieces have legs but all of this cutting are of 1899 to 1905 manufacture.

Note the curving grace of the bisecting parallel swirls, enclosing partitions of well-defined contiguous stars with unique sprays of leaves or "grain." The fans that hold these delightfully quaint and Victorian motifs together are usually polished and not sharply cut. Because of their rarity and unusual charm, these older Wheat-pattern pieces are expensive when in mint condition. The decanters are sometimes cut in a swirling design combining only the leaf or grain motif with partitions of single and hob stars.

Bowls, footed

4″	$35.00
6″	38.00
8″	40.00
10″	45.00

29. WHEAT

Item	Price
Bowls, unfooted	
6″	$30.00
8″	35.00
10″	40.00
12″ square	45.00
Box	35.00
Carafe	45.00
Catsup bottle	38.00
Celery dish	35.00
Cologne bottle	32.00
Compote	42.00
Cordial jug	38.00
Cruet	35.00

Cup	$20.00
Decanter	55.00
Goblet	22.00
Jelly dish	35.00
Nappies	
8″	37.00
10″	40.00
Pickle dish	25.00
Pitcher	60.00
Plate	75.00
Punch bowl with stand (rare)	775.00
without stand	550.00
Sauce bottle	25.00
Tumbler	20.00
Wine glass	20.00

30. COMET

All Comet patterns have a similar characteristic. Taking its name from Halley's Comet, the pattern's distinguishing motif is a swirling comet's tail, usually of notched flutes that end in small fans. The swirling comets are combined with star cuttings. In the Hawkes pattern, the stars are 20-point stars combined with 12-point stars—usually five of the larger and four of the smaller on a bowl or nappy.

This pattern is easily recognized. When in doubt, turn the bowl or nappy upside down. The comet characteristic then becomes clear.

Bowl (all sizes)	$40.00
Butter dish with cover	50.00
Carafe	35.00
Celery dish	38.00
Cologne bottle	32.00
Compote	45.00

30. COMET

Item	Price
Cruet	$32.00
Decanter	55.00
Goblet	22.00
Nappy	38.00
Pickle dish	35.00
Pitcher	60.00
Punch bowl	475.00
Sauce dish	35.00
Tumbler	20.00
Wine glass	18.00

See *Cut & Engraved Glass,* pages 294–297.

31. HOLLY WOOD

Note that Holly Wood is two words. It denotes the fragile wood of the holly tree rather than the excitements of a movie capital not dreamed of when this pattern was being cut.

Holly Wood is one of the early patterns, made when cutters were experimenting with the wonders of the curving split. Designers still dared to leave spaces of considerable size uncut. The contiguous fans at the top are charming, accented by the alternating stars and, below, by the smaller fans and hobnail cutting little used in later twentieth-century designs. Cross-hatching and single stars complete the design.

A rare pattern and a particularly pleasing one, it is a challenge for the collector.

Item	Price
Bowls	
6″	$35.00
8″	38.00
10″	42.00
Candlesticks	50.00 a pair
Carafe	45.00
Celery dish	38.00
Cologne	35.00
Compote	42.00
Cruet	38.00
Cup	22.00
Decanter	65.00
Goblet	23.00
Nappies	
6″	28.00
8″	32.00
Olive dish	27.00
Pickle dishes	
oval	32.00
pedestal	35.00
Pitcher	58.00

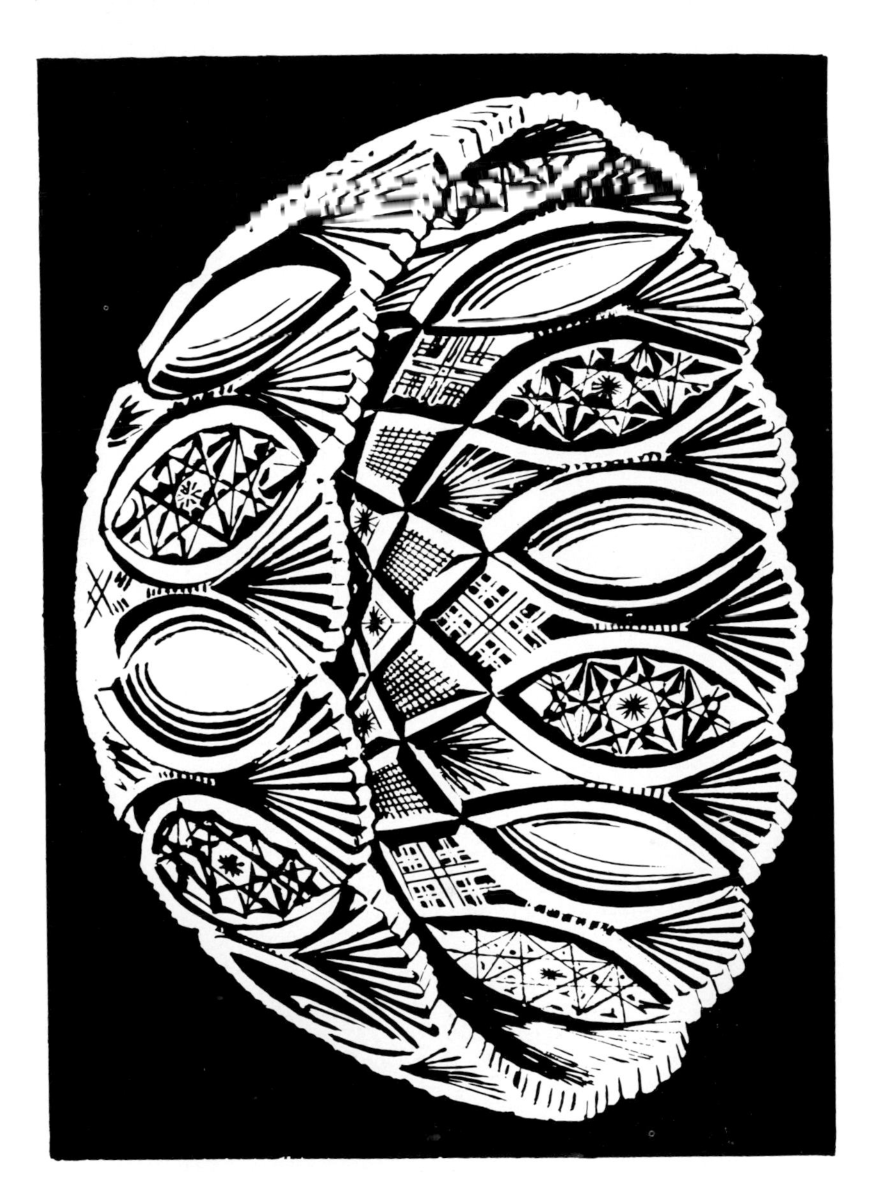

31. HOLLY WOOD

Plate	$78.00
Punch bowl	485.00
Sauce dish	28.00
Tumbler	25.00
Wine glass	20.00

32. GOTHAM

32. GOTHAM

This is an all-over pattern and one cut by many glass houses. It is a nineteenth-century pattern and an elegant one. It follows the Harvard style of well defined, sharp motifs separated by diagonal lines; but, in Gotham, the motifs are hob stars alternating with cross-hatched motifs. Each motif is approximately an inch in diameter, and the dividing lines run diagnonally, forming diamond-shaped areas rather than small squares as is the case in the Harvard.

Gotham is a splendid pattern but, because it was an expensive one to cut, it is now relatively rare. The metal is always very good. Many Gotham pieces have a handsome border of interlacing hob stars, a distinguishing characteristic of the pattern. Harvard pieces have no border.

Item	Price
Bowls	
4″	$22.00
6″	25.00
8″	38.00
10″ square	45.00
10″ round	42.00
Celery boat	38.00
Cologne	35.00
Compote	25.00
Cruet	38.00
Decanter	45.00
Goblet	20.00
Nappy	40.00
Pitcher	65.00
Plate	55.00
Punch bowl	545.00
Salts	23.00 ea.
Sauce dish	25.00
Sugar bowl	37.00
Tumbler	18.00
Wine glass	20.00

33. NEWPORT

Here is a pattern that reveals the cutter's skill. It combines chair bottom, fans, single stars, notched prism, hob star, cross-hatching, and deep curving splits into an intricate design in which the dominant motif is a field of interlaced single stars reminiscent of, although different from, the Russian pattern.

Look for the pineapple-shaped area in the design, which is partitioned to contain the center band of interlaced single stars, two bands of notched prisms, and two bands of small chair-bottom cutting.

Later copies of Newport (1918) are not as cleanly cut as the earlier originals (1908), but the pattern is nevertheless an expensive one with many fine examples still existing in good condition.

Item	Price
Basket	$125.00
Bowls	
6″	40.00
8″	42.00
10″	45.00
Box	38.00
Candlesticks	50.00 a pair
Celery dish	48.00
Cologne	42.00
Compote	77.00
Cruet	43.00
Decanter	64.00
Goblet	30.00
Nappy	45.00
Pitcher	75.00
Punch bowl	750.00
Salts	20.00 ea.
Sugar bowl, with cover	45.00
Sauce dish	25.00
Tumbler	30.00
Wine glass	25.00

33. NEWPORT

Pitcher	$55.00
Plate	65.00
Punch bowl	485.00
Sauce bottle	38.00
Sauce dish	32.00
Sherbet cup	25.00
Tumbler	18.00
Wine glass	15.00

35. PEERLESS

Dominated by a center hob star, Peerless is a brilliant and sparkling pattern, cut between 1905 and 1915. The hob-star motif is framed by elliptical sections of cross-hatching accented by diamond areas of finely cut chair bottom in deep, exquisite cutting.

Fans complete the bottom of the motif, while long sweeping, interesting miter splits distinguish the top of the design (the use of these two border motifs is reversed on taller pieces, namely punch bowl and stand).

Peerless is a distinguished pattern and particularly attractive to collectors who prefer larger motifs combined with sparkling luster.

Basket	$45.00
Bonbon dish	22.00
Bowls	
6″	18.00
8″	25.00
9″	30.00
10″	35.00
Box	28.00
Carafe	35.00
Celery dish	38.00
Cologne bottle	35.00
Compote	45.00

35. PEERLESS

Cordial jug	$42.00
Cruet	35.00
Cup	20.00
Decanter	48.00
Goblet	25.00
Jelly dish with handle	28.00
Nappies	
6″ olive	25.00
8″ pickle	30.00

Item	Price
Pitchers	
straight	$45.00
globe	58.00
Plate	42.00
Punch bowl	550.00
Sauce dish	28.00
Sherbet cup	25.00
Tumbler	18.00
Wine glass	12.00

36. STEUBEN

Named for the county in New York State of which Corning is the seat, Steuben is a distinguished pattern in cut glass.

The Hawkes Company, which originally cut Steuben in 1903, began making its own blanks of fine metal at what was called the Steuben Glass Works. Many pieces still carry the small Steuben etched mark on foot or base.

Later (1933), Steuben became the name of a subsidiary of the Corning Glass Company. Under the direction of Arthur Armory Houghton, Jr., Steuben became the trademark of exquisite and matchless American contemporary glass.

The early Steuben pattern has an easily identified characteristic. The feet of stemmed ware, the necks of decanters, pitchers, and bottles, and the feet of compotes are cut in well-defined, 6-sided flutes. Stemmed pieces have scalloped bases.

The pattern was one of the first to use the ever-after popular saw-toothed scallop at the top rim of open pieces. It is a classic example of an older form (1840) of cutting through a background cutting.

Using an inverted fan and predominant cane-bottom motif, the Steuben is singular for its two parallel miter splits cleanly dividing the design into upper, center, and lower sections.

Because of its highly individualized characteristics, Steuben is not easily combined with other patterns.

36. STEUBEN

Bowls	
6″	$25.00
8″	30.00
10″	38.00
Butter dish	40.00
covered	48.00
Compote	
5″ diameter, 4½″ high	32.00
6″ diameter, 5″ high	38.00
7″ diameter, 8″ high	42.00
8″ diameter, 7″ high	45.00
Cruet	38.00

Cup	$20.00
Decanter	55.00
Goblet	30.00
Ice bucket with tray	65.00
Jelly dish with handle	35.00
Jug with handle	42.00
Nappies	
8″ preserves	39.00
10″ oblong	41.00
Pitcher	55.00
Plate	75.00
Punch bowl	650.00
Sherbet cup	25.00
Tumbler	20.00
Wine glass	18.00

37. FLORENCE

A pattern composed of large, well-defined 24-point hob stars and split, bordered bands of cross-hatching, Florence is neither difficult to find nor to identify.

There are usually six large hob stars to the piece and six bands of cross-hatching, although some cutters reduced the number to four or increased the stars to eight. These variations are rare. The splits outlining the predominant stars intersect in a pleasing and graceful border above the pattern to form a finish near the gentle scallops of the top.

Florence was extremely popular and is a relatively simple pattern in an ornate market. It was cut between 1900 and 1910.

Baskets	
small	$32.00
12″	45.00
Bonbon dish	22.00

37. FLORENCE

Bowls	
6″ deep	$25.00
8″ deep	28.00
10″ deep	35.00
Boxes	
powder	25.00
glove	30.00
Catsup bottle	22.00
Celery dish	24.00
Cologne	26.00
Compote	28.00

Item	Price
Cordial	$30.00
Cruet	25.00
Cup	18.00
Decanter	45.00
Goblet	20.00
Ice bucket with plate	42.00
Jelly dish	24.00
Jug	32.00
Nappies	
6″	28.00
8″	30.00
Pickle dish	22.00
stemmed	28.00
Pitcher	43.00
Plate	62.00
Punch bowl	425.00
Sauce bottle	32.00
Sherbet cup	21.00
Tumbler	20.00
Vases, depending on size and shape	40.00 to 125.00
Wine glass	18.00

See *Cut & Engraved Glass,* pages 215–217.

38. ARGAND

The dominant characteristic of Argand is a graceful movement produced by twin bands, one cut in cross-hatching, the other in an intricate notching. The two bands swing across the bottom of the open pieces, enclosing a central star, and rise to the terminus or the rim to enclose a large hob star that is alternated with a quadrant of single-star motifs.

The distinguishing characteristic of Argand (1900–1910), as in other ornate cuttings, sometimes does not appear identical on pieces of varying shapes (i.e., carafes and celery boats). This

38. ARGAND

is the running together of the two bands through the pattern, each with its own motif cutting. But look for these two motifs and you won't go wrong on Argand.

Item	Price
Bowls	
6″	$25.00
8″	28.00
10″	30.00
Box (powder)	35.00
Butter dish with cover	45.00
Carafe	42.00
Castup bottle	32.00
Celery dish	35.00
Cologne	42.00
Compote	45.00
Cordial	41.00
Cruet	38.00
Cup	20.00
Decanter	55.00
Goblet	23.00
Jelly dish with handles	32.00
Jug	35.00
Nappies	
6″ olive	24.00
8″ preserves	28.00
Oval pickle dish	32.00
Pitcher	67.00
Plate	75.00
Punch bowl with stand	575.00
Tumbler	20.00
Wine glass	18.00

39. ARABESQUE

What a treasure a collection of Arabesque would be!

Here is an old pattern, from the early years of the Brilliant Period, that combines the smaller earlier motifs of the period with miter bands which required the ultimate in cutting skill.

39. ARABESQUE

The field is Russian, that is, a continuous combination of hob and small stars, cut through by gracefully curving arabesques of parallel miter splits. The area between the parallels is carefully notched. In decanters and bottles, the parallel splits merge into a notched-prism effect on the neck.

This was an expensive pattern and not extensively cut because of the great skill required in its intricate cutting.

Bowls	
7″	$40.00
8″	45.00
10″	54.00
Celery dishes	
vase	62.00
boat	48.00
Compote	62.00
Cruet	41.00
Cup	25.00
Decanter	68.00
Goblet	38.00
Nappies	
6″	33.00
8″	37.00
Pitcher	75.00
Plate	140.00
Punch bowl with stand	675.00
Tumbler	35.00
Wine glass	28.00

40. NEW BRILLIANT

A truly "brilliant" combination of notched prism and enclosed hob stars, with fans on the larger pieces, this is an exclusive Libbey pattern. Appearing on the market about 1910, New Brilliant is pictured in catalogue and magazine advertisements of that date and remained a standard Libbey pattern for years.

Although it was cut on glass of weight, clarity, and quality equal to that used for patterns of more intricate design, New Brilliant was one of the less expensive Libbey patterns. This with its brilliance made it one of the most popular patterns of the many cut in the early twentieth century.

Easily identified by its combination of enclosed hob star and notched prisms, it is collectible in a variety of pieces.

Item	Price
Berry bowls	
9″	$40.00
10″	45.00
Candlesticks, 10″	35.00 ea.
Carafes (water bottles)	60.00
Celery tray	50.00
Cologne bottles	
9 ounces	35.00
12 ounces	45.00
Compotes, stemmed	
6½″ diameter, 8″ high	65.00
6½″ diameter, 11½″ high	85.00
Cream pitcher	30.00
Cruet	38.00
Cup (punch)	15.00
Decanters	
pint	38.00
quart	45.00
Finger bowl	25.00
Flower centers (Vase for the center of the dining table, similar to a carafe but squat with flared top.)	
4″	16.00
6″	32.00
8″	42.00
10″	56.00
12″	88.00
15″	90.00
Goblet	18.00
Ice tub (two handles)	42.00
Loving cup (three handles)	48.00
Nappies	
7″	35.00
8″	40.00
9″	45.00

40. NEW BRILLIANT

10″	$50.00
5″ (one handle)	35.00
Plate, 8″	60.00
Punch bowl	250.00
Salad dressing dish and plate	75.00
Sauce dishes	
5″	22.00
6″	25.00
Spoon tray (square, flat)	40.00
Sugar bowl (two handles)	30.00
Vases	
globe, 10″	35.00
straight, 12″	45.00
tapering	25.00
Water glass	20.00
Whiskey tumbler	25.00
Wine glasses	
Champagne	18.00
Claret	15.00
Madeira	15.00
liqueur	18.00

41. ST. JAMES

An 18-point star enclosing an 8-point star is the striking and easily recognized focal point of this popular design.

The larger star is confined by fans and cross-hatched supporting motifs. The use of the fans top and bottom, all pointing away from the bottom, give St. James a delicate unity.

Much used on tumblers and goblets, St. James was extremely popular for table services. Never a particularly expensive pattern, it was extensively cut on glass of varying degrees of quality all during the Brilliant Period.

Decanters, cologne bottles, and carafes will be found in an amazing variety of shapes.

42. MANITOU

If you like to search, here is a rare pattern to give you a beautiful objective. An expensive pattern, it is also a "sturdy" one.

The central or dominant motif is a 16-point star, squarely framed, with small single stars in the corners. The top of the frame is a V, almost a swag, of polished and tapered pillar cutting, very rare on cut glass of this period (1908–1916). Only Columbia and Crystal City may be said to have this same difficult motif combined with hob star.

A smaller row of hob stars completes the top of the design, forming scallops at the tops of bowls. The bottom of the design rests on bold V motifs neatly cut in rows of nail heads.

Item	Price
Bonbon dish	$30.00
Bowls	
6″	35.00
8″	38.00
10″	42.00
Carafe	50.00
Celery dish	42.00
Cologne bottle	38.00
Compote	42.00
Cruet	35.00
Cup	26.00
Decanter	65.00
Goblet	30.00
Nappies	
6″	28.00
7″	34.00
8″	38.00
Pitcher	72.00
Plate	80.00
Punch bowl	650.00
Tumbler	25.00
Wine glass	22.00

42. MANITOU

43. CHAMPION

43. CHAMPION

Like many patterns where the large hob star is dominant, this pattern has a deeply cut or "knobby" look when seen from the sides of the bowls. Easily recognized on the bottom of nappies, bowls, and smaller olive dishes, the design is a combination of the 24-point hob star and diagonal splits; the bisected areas created by the splits are cross-hatched. The upper hob stars form top scallops alternating with fans.

Although Champion is not in any way as elaborate or as costly a pattern as Marquise or Limoge (cut at about the same time, between 1905 and 1915), it presents a rich appearance because of the elevation of the larger hob star near the rim of the open vessels. Collectors of the 24-hob-star patterns will find Champion rewarding because of the great variety of pieces cut in this pattern.

In large pieces, such as punch bowls, the cross-hatched areas and miters appear as swags between two rows of large hob stars.

Item	Price
Basket	$45.00
Bonbon dish (cut in many shapes—3-leaf clovers, hearts, etc.)	20.00
Bowls	
6″	28.00
8″	30.00
10″	35.00
12″	42.00
Boxes	
powder	38.00
handkerchief	45.00
jewelry	45.00
Butter dish with cover	50.00
Carafe	55.00
Catsup bottle	35.00
Celery dish	40.00

Cheese dish with cover	$55.00
Cologne bottle	45.00
Compotes	
6″ high, 8″ diameter	38.00
8″ high, 10″ diameter	42.00
Cordial jug	35.00
Cruet	30.00
Cup	20.00
Decanters	
quart	50.00
pint	38.00
half-pint	30.00
Goblet	20.00
Ice bowl	32.00
Jelly dishes	
stemmed	28.00
with handles	25.00
Nappies	
8″ preserves	28.00
6″ olive	22.00
Pitcher	
straight	45.00
globe	48.00
Plate	52.00
Punch bowl	525.00
Sauce bottle	35.00
Sauce dish	28.00
Tumbler	22.00
Wine glass	20.00

44. YUCATAN

This is an elaborate cutting which is spectacular in its brilliance. Expensive to cut, it did not stand the vicissitudes of time (it was cut between 1908 and 1912), cracking along the intricately bisecting splits. Only on the bottom of nappies or bowls can the ingenious use of the curving split be recognized. From the side, Yucatan is a brilliant composite motif in which six 12-point single stars cluster around a center single star. The intermediate motif is a cone of cross-hatching.

On the bottoms of nappies, the primary splits that contain the central hob star are easily identified.

Item	Price
Basket	$125.00
Bonbon dish	38.00
Bowls	
6″	42.00
8″	45.00
9″	50.00
10″	60.00
Box (powder)	65.00
Butter dish with cover	75.00
Carafe	60.00
Catsup	42.00
Celery dish	45.00
Colognes	
globe	38.00
straight	42.00
Compote	
6″	42.00
8″	45.00
10″	48.00
Cordial jug	45.00
Cruet	55.00
Cup	25.00
Decanter	65.00

44. YUCATAN

Item	Price
Goblet	$25.00
Ice bucket	75.00
Jelly dish	32.00
Nappies	
6″	35.00
8″	42.00
10″	48.00
Pitcher	75.00
Plate	100.00
Punch bowl with stand	875.00
Sauce bowl	62.00
Tumbler	30.00
Wine glass	25.00

45. LIMOGE

At the turn of the century, any pattern the principal unit of which was a circular cluster of small hob stars was called Limoge. Various cutting houses used their own favorite design motifs to hold Limoge together, but often the cluster of six hob stars was surrounded by curving bands of chain bottom and cross-hatching, with a larger hob star at the base.

Look for the circle of six small hob stars. Limoge is easy to identify, particularly on punch bowls, compotes, celery dishes, and nappies. It is usually a sharp cutting, cut on good heavy metal.

Item	Price
Basket	$55.00
Bowls	
6″	28.00
8″	35.00
10″	42.00
12″ with small pedestal	48.00
Box	35.00
Celery dish	32.00
Cologne bottle	35.00
Compotes	
14″ high, 9″ diameter	62.00
12″ high, 9″ diameter	60.00
10″ high, 8″ diameter	58.00
9″ high, 7″ diameter	52.00
8″ high, 6″ diameter	48.00
Cruet	48.00
Cup	20.00
Decanter	55.00
Goblet	20.00
Jelly dish (flat)	22.00
Nappy	38.00
Pickle dish with pedestal	30.00
Pitcher	65.00
Plate (rare)	85.00

46. MARQUISE

Punch bowl	$550.00
Sauce dish (bonbon)	32.00
Syrup jug	35.00
Tumbler	20.00
Wine glass	18.00

47. VICTORIA

The Victoria is an old and fairly simple pattern. Twenty-point stars are cut to fill rectangles which seem, from the reverse side, to be joined by bow ties of cross-hatching.

The open areas of the pattern give it a light simplicity that is most pleasing, particularly on the stemmed ware. Rows of hob stars are regularly placed to form a band around the tops of bowls.

The distinguishing characteristic of Victoria is the "bow tie."

Item	Price
Bowls	
8″	$30.00
9″	35.00
10″	38.00
Box with lid	35.00
Carafe	42.00
Catsup bottle	35.00
Celery dish	42.00
Cologne bottle	45.00
Compote	38.00
Cordial jug	40.00
Cruet	30.00
Cup	20.00
Decanter	55.00
Goblet	25.00
Jelly dish	32.00
Nappies	
6″	24.00
8″	32.00
Pickle dish	
oval	32.00
pedestal	35.00
Pitcher	50.00
Plate	65.00

48. MORGAN

Pickle dish	$28.00
Pitcher	48.00
Plate	67.00
Punch bowl	525.00
Tumbler	15.00
Wine glass	24.00

49. ROSETTE

This is a rare pattern and given here because of its unusual and dominant figure, the rosette. The center of the motif is a hob star, the outer rim is literally a rosette of notched prisms terminating in small fans. It is combined with small 8-point stars in lozenge-shaped, cross-hatched areas. Chair bottom ties the base of the pattern together, fans complete the top.

An expensive pattern, Rosette was cut on luxury pieces such as punch bowls with stands, goblets, and large flat bowls. Usually cut on nineteenth-century or Victorian shapes, the pattern generally has only four rosettes to the piece. The square flat bowls are particularly attractive.

Bowls	
8″	$45.00
10″	55.00
Butter dish with cover	110.00
Compote	72.00
Cup	30.00
Decanter	75.00
Goblet	32.00
Nappies	
8″	45.00
10″	52.00
Pitcher	78.00

49. ROSETTE

Plate (very rare)	$125.00
Punch bowl	1,025.00
Tumbler	30.00
Wine glass (rare)	28.00

50. PINWHEEL

The Pinwheel in all its variations is the most popular (and also the most common) of the twentieth-century patterns.

The Pinwheel was combined with other motifs in great variety, but the central motif is so distinctive that it dominates the pattern. Illustrated is one of the earliest Pinwheels. Here it is combined with a good hob-star center and triangle motifs of Strawberry-Diamond with double fan.

The prices listed are for this older Pinwheel, cut on good metal. The pattern declined toward 1910 and late Pinwheel variants can be had for somewhat less than the prices quoted here for the older standard Pinwheel patterns.

Some manufacturers used Whirlwind as the title for their Pinwheel patterns.

Item	Price
Basket	$45.00
Bonbon dish	28.00
Bowls	
6″	22.00
8″	28.00
9″	32.00
10″	35.00
Box (covered powder)	38.00
Butter dish	40.00
Carafe	45.00
Celery dish	35.00
Cologne	38.00
Compote	40.00
Cordial	42.00
Cruet	49.00
Cup	20.00
Decanter	48.00
Goblet	25.00

Item	Price
Jelly dishes	
with handles	$28.00
pedestal	34.00
Nappies	
6″	30.00
8″	35.00
Pickle dish, oblong	35.00
Pitcher	55.00
Plate	65.00
Punch bowl	425.00
Sauce dish	28.00
Tumbler	25.00
Wine glass	20.00

See *Cut & Engraved Glass*, pages 291–293, and Index.

50. PINWHEEL